Mylie's Lyme Story

By Alexandra and Madeline Castellanos

Illustrations by Anne Zimanski

Printed in the United States of America

First Printing, 2020

ISBN 978-0-578-74660-9

For Madeline, without you this book would not have happened. And Emmanuel, for your cleverness with words.

One hot summer day while I was playing fetch with my dog Max, my mom noticed a large red rash on my arm.

"Mylie, where did this rash come from? Does it hurt?"

If you knew my mom, you would know she always has a million questions.

"No, Mom, everything is fine. It's just hot out!"

But my mom didn't feel everything was "fine," so she phoned Dr. Kurtz right away.

My mom explained that she was taking me to see Dr. Kurtz because of the rash's shape, which looked like a circle inside another circle, like a bull's-eye.

After examining my rash, Dr. Kurtz suggested we draw my blood.

"Draw blood for a rash? No way!"

With Dr. Kurtz and my mom staring at me, it seemed there was no way out of it.

I took a deep breath and declared, **"Fine, I'll do it!"**

Dr. Kurtz said, "Thank you for being brave, Mylie. Maybe your mom can treat you to ice cream after?"

On the way to get my much-deserved ice cream reward, I could not stop staring at my bull's-eye rash. I worried that other people would notice it. I wondered if it would ever go away!

Mom must have been reading my mind, because just then, she looked at me and said, "Mylie, give it time. Dr. Kurtz said the rash should clear up by the end of this week."

Phew!

A few days later Mom and I went back to Dr. Kurtz's office to discuss my results. He discovered that I had something called Lyme disease.

"Lyme disease!" I screamed.

"But I don't even
like limes!"

"Am I going to turn
green? Did I eat too
many veggies?"

So many thoughts ran
through my head.

If I could be excused from
eating peas and broccoli
forever, then maybe having
Lyme wouldn't be such a crime!

Mom sat there with a look of surprise. She asked,
"How did Mylie get Lyme? And what is this disease?"

Dr. Kurtz explained to us that I in fact had NOT eaten too
many vegetables, but I had been bitten by a bug with a ton
of germs.

Yuck!

This evil bug that bit me had bacteria called *Borrelia* living inside of it. *Borrelia* is a cork-screw-shaped (*spirochete*) bacteria that travels quickly and deep into the body.

It can make a person experience brain fog, body aches, fevers and more.

"I'll go ahead and write Mylie a prescription. She'll need to start as soon as possible in order to get better," Dr. Kurtz said.

"A prescription?! That means I have to take medicine!" I said dreadfully while slouching in the chair.

Another yuck!

On our way back home, we had one more stop to make. Mom assured me that this detour would be quick.

As we finally reached home, I kicked off my shoes, turned on the TV and went in the kitchen for a snack.

Then mom called me over and said, "Ready to kick Lyme's butt? Hi-ya!"

Since my diagnosis, I've become gluten-free. This means I avoid certain foods that upset my tummy.

But don't worry, there are plenty of options for me, including ice cream!

Although I take my medicine and eat better, there are days I do not feel like myself. Some days, schoolwork is difficult to finish and I'm too exhausted to play with my friends.

Dr. Kurtz said these feelings would not last forever.

My Lyme journey isn't over yet, but I'm still a normal kid with BIG dreams.

Mom called me from the kitchen,
"Mylie, did you take the
trash out?"

See, I told you I'm still a normal kid.

Glossary

Borrelia burgdorferi: The bacteria that most commonly causes Lyme disease (named after William Burgdorfer, the American scientist who discovered it).

Erythema migrains: Rash in the shape of a bulls-eye, usually associated with exposure to *Borrelia burgdorferi*.

Spirochetes (SPY-ruh-keets): The group of spiral-shaped bacteria that includes *Borrelia burgdorferi*, which causes Lyme disease.

Co-infections: Common within Lyme disease, co-infections may cause severe symptoms and require treatment. There are more than 350 co-infections associated with *Borrelia* (Lyme disease). Please talk to your doctor about getting tested for these.

Herxheimer reaction: The body's response to a detox.

Lyme literate medical doctor (LLMD): A doctor specifically educated in *Borrelia burgdorferi* and Borrelia bacterial families.

Lyme disease name origins: Lyme disease began as a mysterious illness afflicting adults and children in the 1970s in Old Lyme, Connecticut.

For more information about and help for Lyme disease:

ILADS.org has a registry of Lyme literate medical doctors

Financial Assistance:
- Alex Hudson Lyme Foundation
- LymeLight Foundation
- LymeAid 4 Kids
- LivLyme Foundation
- Ticked Off Foundation
- Global Lyme Alliance

Lyme and Co-Infections Labs:
- IGeneX
- LabCorp
- Galaxy Diagnostics
- Quest Diagnostics
- DNA Connections

Tick Removal Kit:
- Tickit

Important note: Although a bulls-eye rash is the preliminary symptom described in this book, it does not occur in many cases of Lyme disease. Other preliminary symptoms can include: Fever, chills, headache, fatigue, muscle and joint aches, and swollen lymph nodes. Please consult your doctor if you have any symptoms or concerns.

Printed in the USA
CPSIA information can be obtained
at www.ICGtesting.com
CBHW041653210324
5487CB00107B/127